D1095206

The
Book of
Humorous
Medical
Anecdotes

The Book of Humorous Medical Anecdotes

Compiled by
Susi Greenwood

SPRINGWOOD BOOKS
ASCOT, BERKSHIRE

First published 1989 by Springwood Books Limited
Springwood House, The Avenue, Ascot, Berkshire

ISBN 0 86254 142 5

Designed and Typeset by Hybert Design and Type, Maidenhead
Printed and bound in Great Britain by
Jolly & Barber Limited, Rugby

Foreword

*T*he Evelina Children's Hospital at Guy's is a large unit with over 100 beds, 8 wards including the Special Care Baby Unit and Intensive Care facilities especially for children. The hospital treats both local patients living in South East London and children from all over England who are suffering from complex neurological, kidney and heart conditions. Inevitably the unit is a very busy one with many committed staff all with the common aim of providing the best possible care for sick children.

The appeal was set up in 1983 to ease the increasing difficulties with funding and to supplement available government monies. It has been used over the past six years to provide intensive care equipment and other much needed items and more recently to provide for the direct costs of running two intensive care cots in our Paediatric Cardiology Unit. Over time our reliance on additional funding of this type has increased, we have now reached £1 million of a £3 million target! We have just embarked on our new Sponsor-a-Cot campaign in a renewed effort to achieve our target.

The Appeal Committee are delighted that Springwood Books Ltd are supporting the Appeal through their publication "The Book of Humorous Medical Anecdotes", and thank readers for the interest shown.

Professor Michael Tynan MD FRCP
Chairman of the Evelina Children's Hospital Appeal

List of Contributors

J.C. Ainley-Walker
G.W. Allan
G.S. Andrews
R.J. Andrews
D.W. Barron
R.W. Barter
H.N. Baylis
J.R. Bennett
J.P. Bentley
R.M. Bernstein
P.G. Bevan
P.C. Bewes
R.C. Bickerton
M.H.S. Bound
M. Burke
W.D.B. Darbishire
V.A. Harvey
B. Isaacs
G.M. Jolly
A. Lee
A.K. Mant
R.T. Marcus
A. Martin
R.N. Matthews
E. Mendus-Edwards
P.H. Merry
D.P. Mikhailidis
A.R.O. Miller
C.G. Miller
T.G. Milliken

J.F.O. Mitchell
D.A. Moffat
B. Montgomery
W.N. Morley
J.B. Morrison
J. Munro
Sir Reginald Murley
G.A.W. Neill
N.D. Noah
W.J. O'Connell
B. O'Donnell
J.J. O'Sullivan
N.C. Oswald
F.S. Pagan
A.W. Pengelly
J.A. Powis
T.L.C. Pratt
L. Pritchett
by kind permission of GP Magazine
J.W. Rae
E. Sharpe
K. Taylor
J.P. Town
P. Tyrer
J.D. Whitby
A.F. Winder

Acknowledgements

*T*he response to the request for anecdotes from consultants, doctors and nurses has been overwhelming and I am indebted to all who sent contributions. This book represents the very best and my warmest thanks go to those contributors.

I should particularly like to thank Punch for permission to reproduce several of their cartoons.

S.G.

I met Harold's wife long before I met Harold. She was a mountainous lady, and she gradually worked her way through all those ailments with which mountainous ladies are plagued: her gallstones were, I am glad to say, cured by removing them. Her bad back was less easy, but with a judicious mix of painkillers, corsets and physiotherapy, it could at least be made tolerable. Her breathlessness she treated herself by not doing anything that would make her breathless. But it was only when her legs started to give out under the strain of it all that she started to need home visits and I became aware of Harold.

Even then I did not often catch him in. He worked as a postman and left home at some unearthly hour in the morning. Occasionally when returning from a visit on a winter's night I would catch sight of him on his bicycle, pedalling to work through the freezing fog – on his way to sort *my* letters, perhaps – and I would feel guilty as I headed home to my nice warm bed.

He was a wizened little man with a face that looked as if it had been squashed to one side, this appearance being exaggerated by the rather ill-fitting glass eye on his other side. His wife dominated him totally.

'Get my mint humbugs, Harold,' she would say as soon as he had sat down. Then it would be, 'Where did I put my glasses?'. 'Does the cat want to go out?'. 'Fetch me a handkerchief'. And all this while I was there. I shuddered to imagine what must have passed between them when they were, so to speak, consenting adults in private.

Yet every morning Harold got up at four o'clock to earn money for this idle, bullying woman. Was it really devotion to duty – or might it just be his form of escapism?

She was the only lady I have ever met who had a large cupboard full of food upstairs in her bedroom. When I ventured to remark on this idiosyncracy she explained that it was in case she got hungry in the night, her tone of voice suggesting that everyone had a food cupboard in their bedroom. But she continued to assure me that she hardly ate a thing and could not understand why she was putting on weight.

Another curious fact I discovered after a while was that she was a wrestling fanatic. She knew all their names – Big Daddy, Giant Haystacks, The Skull – and would spend hours watching them on video. But Harold once told me that her favourites were the Sumo wrestlers. These were her heroes. Despite her shortness of breath, I would have put my money on her against them any time.

Then one day Harold came to see me about himself. He had hurt his shoulder. At first he was evasive about how it had happened, but eventually he admitted, rather shamefacedly, that his wife had put him in an arm-lock after he had burned the dinner.

He had a frozen shoulder. He also had a bruise

on his cheek and his artificial eye was looking the wrong way. He was a sorry sight.

He tried to carry on working, but found he could not sort his letters. Reluctantly he went on the sick and, perhaps as a result of the twenty-four hours a day exposure to his wife that this brought, looked more and more miserable. His shoulder got steadily worse.

The days off work turned into weeks and the weeks into months. Physiotherapy did not help. Local injections only made the pain worse. Pain-killers made him fall asleep and anti-depressants gave him nightmares. I marvelled how someone who never had a day's illness had been transformed overnight into a broken wreck whose body was screaming, 'I don't want to get better!'.

Then he came to me in tears. He stood to lose his job soon. Surely there was something else he could try? Rather lamely, I suggested psychiatry.

'My wife keeps telling me it's all in the mind. I couldn't stand that'.

'We don't have to tell her,' I suggested gently.

'She'd get it out of me. She always does'. I had visions of her holding him in a half-nelson, perhaps, if she really wanted to torture him, sitting on him until he was gasping for breath and mercy. I wished I could do something to help.

In the end he decided to try some more physiotherapy. I didn't feel very hopeful. It had never worked before.

It was some time before I saw him again, but when he did return he entered with a jaunty air, as if he had just won one of the famed prizes at Mrs. Mobbs' Bingo Hall. Proudly he raised his right arm to point straight up at the ceiling, something he had not done for a long time.

'I told you it would do me good,' he said. 'Can I start work on Sunday?'

I gladly complied, but I remained puzzled by this apparent miracle cure. Reflecting on it afterwards I realised that it could not have been the physiotherapy itself that had cured Harold. It must have happened because he had faith in it and had convinced himself that this time he was going to make it work. I felt rather proud of my analysis of the situation. I wondered whether it was worth a short letter to the *British Medical Journal.*

A few days later I had a call to visit Harold's wife. When I arrived she was waiting for me at the garden gate. She hadn't ventured as far as the garden gate for months – had this miracle cure extended to her as well?

'I'm going to see my solicitor about you,' was her opening shot. Bewildered, I asked what about.

'It's my Harold. You didn't tell me there could be side-effects from this treatment.'

'But I thought the treatment had worked very well. What sort of side-effects?'

'He's buggered off with the physiotherapist!'

Harold and his pretty physiotherapist are married now. I often see them in town, walking hand in hand, obviously very much in love.

Occasionally when I am filling in a physiotherapy request form, I pause and remind myself to consider *all* possible side-effects. But then I carry on writing.

After all, it may have been a side-effect for Harold's wife. But for Harold it was a miracle cure.

'He firmly believes laughter is the
best medicine.'

*'At two hundred and forty quid a week I was
expecting something prettier.'*

One day I was called to a man by his wife. The message simply said that he was dead. When I arrived the man was lying on his bed — cold, pale and still, with his eyes closed.

Being young and trusting I turned to the wife and said, 'Well, I think he has gone, hasn't he?'.

'No, I haven't' said the man opening his eyes.

At this the wife said, 'You mind what the doctor says, he knows best'.

One day, prior to my morning surgery, I received an urgent telephone call to attend a collapsed man.

I rushed to the house and found that the man was dead.

He was living with his brother who was out, so neighbours agreed to find him and let him know.

I returned to the surgery, filled in the death certificate and settled down to my patients.

The first one turned out to be the deceased man's brother, which was exceptional as I had seen neither for some years.

In a solemn and gentle voice I informed him of his brother's demise.

After a short pause the man replied, 'Oh! well, I really came about my toe'.

*I*t was a miserable day with rain skidding across the wet roads. Bradford was shrouded in an inky gloom and the street lights shone prematurely.

Suddenly, through the darkness, I approached an accident. A young motor-cyclist was lying in the road, his cycle crumpled on the pavement.

I leaped from my car, rendered him first aid and made him as comfortable as possible. He had a fractured leg and several abrasions. Someone else had sent for an ambulance.

After five minutes another doctor arrived and we discovered that we had been at the same medical school. We chatted and reminiscences flowed freely.

We were interrupted by someone tugging at my arm.

It was a Catholic priest.

He pushed through and knelt by the young man who was looking rather pale by now.

'Are you a Catholic?' the priest asked. He looked as if he was about to tender the last rites.

'Yes, Father,' muttered the young man.

'Ah! So much the worse,' sighed the priest, 'It was me who knocked you over.'

Professor: 'What does the carotid sinus do?'

Student: 'It measures the blood pressure, Sir.'

Professor (sarcastic): 'Yes, I suppose it prints it on a ticket and passes it out of the urethra!'.

'Now, here's one that I stitched up earlier.'

*T*he dignified Professor of Surgery was sitting at the table in his Outpatient Clinic interviewing patients before examining them. He prided himself in taking the detailed history of each personally and writing it out in longhand in the notes. The next patient was an elderly man slightly hard of hearing.

Professor: 'And what is wrong with you, Mr Jones?'

Mr Jones: 'I've got a bad pain in my tum.'

The ring of students around the table craned their necks forward expectantly to catch every word.

Professor: 'Did it come on suddenly?'

Mr Jones: 'No, on Saturday.'

*T*he ward round stopped beside the bed of an elderly man. The house-physician explained that the patient had been admitted in a severely confused state, and had not yet shown improvement. He was also rather deaf. The consultant decided to test for himself the patient's mental state; to questions about his name, address and current whereabouts incorrect or incomprehensible information was forthcoming. The consultant tried once more: 'What's your date of birth?' he bellowed. '6th of July' came the answer. The consultant smiled thinly to his juniors, hoping they were impressed by his powers of communication. He continued on the same lines: 'What year?' he thundered. The patient also shouted his triumphant and logical reply, 'Every year!'.

*I*n October 1942, on the first day of the battle of El Alamein, the badly wounded feldwebel (sergeant) Beick, from a German armoured division, was admitted to our maxillofacial surgical unit in Aledandria. A shell had struck his tank; he had lost the whole of the lower jaw from angle to angle and, despite transfusion during his evacuation, sergeant Beick was in poor condition. Notwithstanding his severe facial wound he managed to talk remarkably good English. I started a new blood transfusion and, on visiting him a few hours later, he looked up at the bottle of blood and said, 'Is that the fourth bottle, Sir?'. I answered, 'No, feldwebel Beick, it is the fifth'. The German sighed deeply and then responded, 'Oh dear, by the time this transfusion is over I shall not know whether to say Heil Hitler or God Save the King'. During the course of the next few months I came to know Beick quite well but I never detected any further sign of the rather droll sense of humour which he had displayed on that day when we first met. Perhaps it had all been due to the five bottles of good British blood.

*M*r V, a well known GU Surgeon, was a keen fisherman and spent as much time as possible on the river bank. A fellow angler with whom he was acquainted consulted him about his dribbling in-continence and other anti-social symptoms, and was admitted for prostatectomy. Mr V performed the operation with his usual dexterity and the patient was discharged home in the regulation time.

Some few weeks later a parcel arrived at the hospital addressed to Mr V, who on opening it discovered a beautiful salmon trout. This was accompanied by a note from his fellow angler thanking him for his skill and attention and asking him to accept, as a token of gratitude, 'The first fish I have caught with a dry fly'.

Within a few weeks, two patients came complaining of breathlessness following a chest injury some years before, which had left them with extensive calcification of the pleura on one side. By a coincidence, each had sustained his injury when falling down a manhole.

Some months later a labourer in his fifties and his formidable wife came to see me. He also had pleural calcification following a chest injury. 'You must have fallen down a manhole' I suggested. Whilst he was vehemently denying this, his wife interrupted him saying, 'How do you know you have never fallen down a manhole? Look at the state you come home in on Saturday nights. You could easily have fallen down one without remembering anything about it.'

*'It's millions of years since **He** created the
perfect machine and we're still waiting for a
comprehensive spare part service.'*

Young boy patient with multiple lacerations on arms following glass window pane accident. Stitched up successfully by doctor.

Boy to doctor: 'Will I be able to play the violin after all this?'

Doctor: 'Yes of course you will.'

Boy: 'That's funny, because I never could before.'

Many years ago, while on duty in the Medical Department in an occupational health setting, I noticed a lot of commotion on the radio generated by the security man pressing an electronic button to open the gates of the factory to allow access to a bin lorry, which was coming at high speed towards the gates.

It transpired that, amongst the rubbish collected by the bin crew, there was a plastic bottle with some bleach in the bottom of it. The crusher on the lorry squeezed the bottle and a jet of bleach hit one of the binmen in the eye. The others quickly put him in the cab and, knowing of the existence of this occupational health department, headed off at high speed for the factory. The man was brought into the department and presented to me. I had a quick look at his eye and realized the need for urgent 'eyewash'. I then explained to the man that I wanted to wash out his eye with water whereupon he forced his way out of the chair., passed me and ran out of the building shouting, 'Nobody is taking my eye out to wash it'. The security man at the gate had alerted his colleagues who turned up in the van and as our binman was running down the front steps he was carried back into the building and sat upon. This facilitated the carrying out of the required emergency eyewash.

Years ago a friend of mine went for the London Membership examination. At that time, rather than all the long cases being acute medical cases as most of them are now, a number of them were professional examination cases, people with chronic conditions, magnificent signs but not terribly ill, and they tended to go up to the exam for many years.

My friend, who was in a parallel branch of medicine, pathology, decided that it would help him enormously to have the Membership of the College of Physicians. He rather doubted if he had the clinical expertise to pass the exam but knew that doing well in the long case would help him a great deal. He therefore set about, over eighteen months, seeing every examination case that he could track down in the whole of the London area. When he went into the exam he felt that he had succeeded, for of six cases he had actually seen and examined five of them. But to his horror the examiner started leading him to the only case he hadn't seen. He said, 'Sir, I think I should tell you that I have seen this case before', and so receiving a pat on the back he was taken to a case that he really had seen before and I may say passed with flying colours.

'Spare a few pence towards an eye test, Sir.'

Surgeons and anaesthetists enjoy, if that is the word, a special relationship.

A surgeon usually has no difficulty in pinpointing the cause of his present operative problems. It is the anaesthetist.

One such troubled surgeon, deep in a surgical swamp, turned in desperation to the anaesthetist who was sitting calmly at the head of the table and said, 'You must be the worst anaesthetist in Ireland'. The anaesthetist was unfased and merely blew the air out of the syringe and said, 'That would be too much of a coincidence'.

When I was a registrar in paediatrics at the Birmingham Children's Hospital it was the custom in this particular 'firm' for the juniors to see the bulk of the follow-ups during the Outpatient Clinics while the consultant would see the bulk of the new referrals. Whenever there was a gap in the follow-ups the junior staff would sit in with the 'boss' to pick up the pearls of wisdom which would fall from his lips. He was a paediatrician of great renown, silver haired and benign, nearly always with a twinkle behind his half-moon glasses.

Birmingham is a multi-ethnic community and on this occasion a young West Indian boy, Sam, had been referred by his GP for a persistent cough. He was a small 'well-padded' boy and he was accompanied by his mother who might best be described (and I do not

'Here comes our doctor now.
He'll give you the blood test.'

use the description pejoratively) as 'a big West Indian Momma.'

In his questioning of Sam's mother the boss, being mindful of the possibility of asthma, asked the question, 'Tell me, Mother, when Sam coughs does he wheeze?', only to receive the clinic-stopping reply of 'sho' does, Doc, all down his leg.' Virtual end of Outpatient Clinic.

A well known playwright with bouts of acute mania was the most difficult patient in the psychiatric unit. The only activity that kept him in a reasonable mood was to read plays.

One morning the MO on duty called at the Medical Superintendent's office and said 'Mr X Sir in Room 100 is in a terrible state and we have simply nothing left for him to read'.

After looking around his office and bookshelves without success the Superintendent spotted the London Telephone Directory and, picking it up, said 'Look, hand him this and see what happens'.

Several days passed and not a sound was heard. So much was his curiosity aroused that the Superintendent went to see for himself.

'Well, Mr X', he said 'how goes it?' Mr X sighed and put down the Directory. 'Well Sir', he said, 'I haven't really started the play but my, what a cast!'

A rather self-opinionated senior surgical registrar in a teaching hospital was examining a patient whom he considered had been very badly managed prior to his recent transfer from a provincial district general hospital. He was complaining bitterly to the house staff about the mismanagement and decided to telephone the referring hospital to express his displeasure. Thinking that he was talking to a junior registrar he let fly with a torrent of abuse at the handling of the patient. Unfortunately he was in fact talking to the senior surgical consultant at the referring hospital who happened to be both highly placed and influential in the hierarchy of the Royal College of Surgeons. At the end of the tirade the consultant said, 'Do you know who you are speaking to?' and when the senior registrar replied in the negative he was informed in no uncertain terms.

Silence for a moment and then the senior registrar said 'Do you know who you are speaking to?'. When the consultant said 'No' he merely heard the word 'Good' and the click of the disconnected telephone!

A clinical tutor wishing to describe the five crepitations heard through the stethoscope in pulmonary tuberculosis, used to advise students it was just like rubbing hair between finger and thumb near your ear. One day, absent-mindedly looking at the bevy of female students at the front of the class, he suggested the sound of fine crepitations was just like the sound of hair rubbing between your legs.

*P*atient with flatulence was consulting his GP and indeed passed flatus during the consultation. The doctor went into a cupboard and reappeared with a long rod. 'What are you going to do with that Doctor?' 'I'm going to open the window!'

*T*he examiner was trying to get the medical student to use the phrase 'pressure necrosis' but without success. Eventually the examiner, frustrated, whipped off his spectacles and pointed to the bridge of his nose where the spectacles had left a pressure mark. 'What's this, boy?' he barked. The student beamed, as enlightenment at last dawned. 'Ah, you mean congenital syphilis, Sir.'

*M*any years ago a woman brought her well-covered daughter aged fourteen to see me. After they had sat down in my consulting room, I asked the mother:

'What brings you to see me?'

'It's her medistration, doctor,' she said. 'She gets terrible pains every month.'

'Have you given her anything for it?' I enquired.

'Yes,' she said, 'Virginin tablets, but they don't do any good.'

'Sorry, you're back on the waiting list.
In the middle of your operation they had a
call from management to say we'd run out
of funds.'

A Case of Allergy to Panelled Rooms

*T*he day one passes the fellowship examination of one of the Royal Colleges of Surgeons is a memorable experience for every candidate, but on this particular occasion it was an unforgettable event for the examiners too.

It is early evening and the anxious participants gather in the entrance hall of the college after an arduous day of clinical examinations, long cases, short cases and vivas with little time for sustenance between. While they anxiously wait, much of the discussion takes place in low nervous tones, the similarity between this experience and that of waiting on 'death row' is compared and contrasted, as others rush off to find the cloakroom. The porter finally appears and begins to read out the numbers of the candidates who have satisfied those hungry lions, the examiners. There are never many and most slink away, empty-handed, disappointed and dejected.

But for the glorious few the celebrations are about to begin. Dazed, they are ushered away down the dimly lit corridor towards the imposing door of the presidential suite. The room is lined with dark oak panelling and at the far end stands the distinguished pride of examiners, now looking almost human as they wait to offer the newly appointed Fellows a glass of sherry. For one of the happy band it has certainly been a gruelling experience, and here he is being entertained by those who only an hour ago held his career in the balance. What a contrast and − with the excitement of passing, the aperitif and nothing to eat all day −

'*I never dreamed the bed shortage was
so acute*'.

quite a mixture. He begins to relax and has another drink.

Sometime later it dawns on him that all of his companions have left, so mumbling an apology he backs unsteadily towards the exit. He tugs at the latch of the door in the panelling to get out, but as it shuts behind him, realizes to his horror that instead of emerging into the corridor he has entered a large broom cupboard, presidential in size, but a broom cupboard all the same. He has two options: either leave immediately and emerge with as much dignity as he can muster, or wait and hope the problem will go away. But the longer he deliberates the sillier he would look coming out. He clutches at a mop for moral support and decides to stay.

Most of the examiners think it's the best thing that has happened all day and want to stay and watch, while others mutter something about falling college standards and the quality of today's applicants. Fortunately for our newly appointed Fellow, standing behind the door in the dark, he hears them all gradually leave. When he is quite sure that the place has emptied, he opens the door and, brushing off the dust and mustering a little dignity, makes his escape, sensitized forever to panelled rooms.

A consultant at an outpatient session was bemoaning the increasing numbers of Sharons, Clints and even a few Cheyannes (named after the current soap-opera heroes and heroines) at the expense of the more traditional Christian names. He was, therefore, delighted to be told by Sister that the little boy who was just coming through the door with his mother was called Robin. As mother and child took their seats he beamed at them and said to all and sundry how pleasant it was to hear a good old-fashioned English name again. Then turning to mother to take down such necessary particulars as surname he opened in his usual fashion by asking 'Now then, Mrs—?', only to receive the devastating reply of 'Mrs Hood'.

*I*n the course of palpation for examination of the respiratory system, the female medical student desired to say that she wished to test for vocal fremitus, where the hand is placed on the chest wall while the patient says 'ninety-nine' or 'one one one' and the examiner decides whether the vibration or fremitus is of normal intensity or not. Unfortunately the young lady could not remember the word fremitus so she suggested to the tutor, 'I will place my hand on him and feel for the buzzing' then triumphantly, as she thought she had remembered the name, 'Phimosis'.

The tutor dryly advised her that phimosis was a condition affecting the foreskin of the penis.

'It was such a lovely evening I thought I'd
just toddle down and have my ears syringed.'

When conducting a lung function study on people exposed to a certain dust at work, at Buxton in Derbyshire several years ago, I encountered a lot of smokers who had lung function problems. I have long since given up telling people not to smoke as they just turn off when you say it, so when one particular gentleman came and I asked him why did he smoke, he retorted that 'I smoke to keep my wife alive, Doctor'. When I asked him to elaborate on this, he said 'If I ever stopped I'd bloody well strangle her'.

A young singlehanded general practitioner was confined to bed with a heavy dose of influenza and had to get a locum, whom he did not know, at short notice. In the middle of the first day's confusion the locum burst into his bedroom and said, 'I've got a chap downstairs who is as mad as a hatter, sign this and we'll get him committed to the mental hospital on a temporary order.' Confused and ill and against his better judgement the practitioner signed the form, relying upon the integrity and competence of his colleague.

Upon his recovery he was alarmed and dismayed to get a letter from solicitors representing the patient, seeking damages for wrongful diagnosis, their client having been discharged from hospital. Of course the locum had completely disappeared. Having carefully

read the evidence, the practitioner could see that there was no concrete evidence of mental disorder, but he felt that the least he could do would be to see the patient again. This was arranged for after surgery late on one winter's evening. On answering the doorbell the doctor could see outlined against the night sky a tall thin figure of middle age with a pointed beard, wearing a dark cloak.

During the course of the interview it became apparent to the doctor that the man appeared completely rational and reasonable. His heart sank. At the end of the interview he asked the man if he would be good enough to sign a record of what had been discussed. The man agreed and signed his name. The doctor picked up the paper and saw that the man had signed 'Charles Roi'. He said to the patient 'I see that you have signed yourself 'Charles Roi'.' The man drew himself up to his full height and, tugging at his pointed beard, said 'Yes. Do you doubt that I am?'. Needless to say the doctor slept peacefully that night.

A female medical student, on her first day of clinical teaching in the wards, was asked about the sequence of examinations of the respiratory system. She ventured, Inspection Palpation, Percussion and Osculation. The teacher pompously advised: 'Miss Brown, osculation is kissing. I do not think the patient would mind but the GMC might prefer you to do auscultation'.

Antenatal Clinic

Obstetrician: 'Ah, Miss ——, good morning.'
Pause.
'I see this will be your fourth child...'

Mother: 'Oh, yais.'

Obstetrician: 'Can you tell me who the father is?'

Mother: 'Oh yais. It's George.'

Obstetrician: Pausing while scanning the notes, then 'George is the father of all your children isn't he?'

Mother: 'Oh, yais.'
Another pause, rather longer.

Obstetrician: 'Tell me, Miss ——, why don't you marry George?'

Mother: 'Oh, – well you see, Doctor, when I was a little girl I had the rheumatic fevers, and my doctor said that I wasn't never to get married.'

As a House Officer in Casualty I occasionally had to certify death in street accidents and such cases which arrived by police ambulence. In one case the child was still alive and was rushed in for resuscitation.

*'It's nothing serious doctor. I'm just feeling
superior, that's all.'*

*'If the Stock Market crashes again, don't
bother trying to revive me.'*

On the next occasion, I was ready with a prompt and speedy reaction; I gathered my stethoscope and ran out to the ambulance, not heeding what the Sergeant said. The latter strolled out after me and repeated 'You'll not need that, Doctor. He's been in Granton Harbour for three weeks!'

*A*s an experienced consultant then in Leicester I was helping out at the Royal Infirmary Department of Pathology's first-ever open day, wearing a white coat and resting between two demonstration sessions.

A lady sidled up to me and said 'Excuse me, are you a consultant or do you work here?'

A consultant urological surgeon was teaching on a ward round and asked a medical student to present a patient's history. This he did, but the consultant wanted to know what the student meant by 'poor urinary stream'. 'How do you mean?' replied the student. 'How does it compare with yours?' asked the consultant. 'Well, well...' stuttered the student. 'Yes, yes' encouraged the consultant from the other side of the bed. There was a pause, and then came the reply, 'I could probably hit you from here, Sir'.

Nasal surgery frequently uses Luc's forceps. During one nasal septum operation under local anaesthetic, I asked Sister on several occasions to pass the Luc's (forceps) please.

When the towels were removed at the finish, I asked the patient if he was all right. 'Yes' he replied, 'I'm fine and felt very little, Doctor, but tell me please, why do you use the soap?' (Lux)

—— • ⌘ • ——

An eighty-four year old farmer came to my Chest Clinic whilst well on the way to recovery from acute bronchitis. I told him he would now get out and about in the good weather that had appeared. He said 'I have already gone back to work'. I replied, 'Surely you do not have to work at your age'. He said, 'I will tell you a story – last week one of my farm hands said to me

You have silver in your hair
You have gold in your pockets
And you have lead in your bottom
And you won't get off your bally tractor.'

So I said, 'Carry on then with the good work'.

If

If you can treat above a score of patients
Before two tedious hours have come and gone,
Stalling the while, on numerous occasions
The importunities of the telephone,
If you can sit, a well-intentioned spider
Incumbent of a stretched and tenuous web
And deal alike with gentleman, outsider,
Malingerer, hypochondriac or scab;
If you can sit, a shabbier Solomon,
Kind, courteous, dispassionate of mood,
Rapt but inscrutable, and follow man
Up hill, down dale, through each vicissitude;
If you'll remind yourself he's only human
Be his behaviour never so bizarre,
Only outdone by that of sister woman
Tho' both expect *you* to be something more;
If you'll receive the younger Rep with courtesy,
With coffee, outstretched hand and bonhomie,
And never say a single word that hurts, he
Won't realize you're due on the first tee!
If you'll prescribe his favoured Beta-Blocker
And read his extract from the BMJ,
'Mong all he woos, you'll be his Lady Docker
A beacon shining in a world astray.
If you can wear your Cinderella garb,
Not envying colleagues in the EEC,
And still remain essentially a Sahib,
Content, with undistorted ECG;
If you can stand, for forty harassing years
The oafishness of the DHSS
You'll be, at last, transcending blood and tears,
The very first Saint of the NHS.

'Oh, Doctor, I have got this terrible headache and an awful pain in my neck and my back aches and my hips hurt me and the rheumatics in my foot are terrible, but I suppose I shouldn't complain because there are thousands worse than me... but they are all dead.'

In this era of resuscitation it may be salutary to tell the following story.

An elderly Irish farmer lay seriously ill and the doctor told the large family that there was no hope. In Ireland this situation is a signal for the relatives and friends to gather to express their sympathy and perhaps in anticipation of the 'wake'. They sat around the kitchen fire while the sick man lay in a box-bed in the shadows at one side, already very quiet and peaceful and apparently not long for this world. As the relatives talked they began to discuss the possibilities of any inheritance and eventually it was decided not to have too much expense at the funeral. This boiled down largely to the number of cars to be hired to follow the hearse which itself was considered essential. There was quite a large family and they first planned to have four cars. However, when the cost was counted, the number was progressively reduced to one and this was agreed. Suddenly a voice came from the sick man in the bed in the shadows saying: 'If yez'll give me ma trousers, I'll walk'.

*'What with flu, transport problems,
ancillaries on strike... scalpel!'*

'Come in here, Miss Fontaine, and sexually harass me!'

A tramp came to the Casualty Department of a hospital complaining of itching in his left ear with a slight deafness. He was seen by a Junior Houseman who looked in the ear and, mystified by what he saw, rang the Ear Nose and Throat Senior Registrar. The tramp was duly seen by the Senior Registrar in the Clinic and his ear was examined under the microscope. The surgeon was amazed when he looked into the ear canal to see two small black eyes, and then the emergence of a rather plump maggot. This was followed by a procession, and he wondered how best to remove these from the ear canal. He tried to use the ear sucker, but the diameter of the maggot was exactly the same as the sucker and this quickly blocked the instrument. The Sister who was standing by suggested that he killed the maggots first by instilling spirit drops into the ear canal.

On hearing the word 'spirit', the tramp sat bolt upright and said, 'Is that "spirit" I hear you say? Don't waste it in my ear, I will drink it'. The Senior Registrar wrote a letter back to the Houseman in Casualty saying, 'Dear Doctor, Thank you very much for sending me this very interesting case of maggotitis media'.

O verheard on Surgical Ward round: 'Physicians are rather like undescended testicles, they are difficult to locate and when they are found, they are pretty ineffective'.

*'Mr. Albert J. Crimpling, and his mid-life
crisis.'*

Ballade of a Frustrated Practitioner

I think I'll misconduct myself today,
I've got so *so* tired of acting ethical.
I'll pour myself three double gins and fall
Flat on my face in Morning Surgery.
I'll get so that I cannot tell a gall-
Stone colic from a Seminal Assay.
It's more than time I met the GMC.
I think I'll misconduct myself today.

I think I'll misconduct myself today,
I'll put an advertisement in the Mail
'Act while there still is time and do not fail;
Make an appointment now with Dr J
Whose therapeutic skill is on a scale
Unparalleled since Osler or McNee'.
I'll take them NHS *and* make them pay.
I think I'll misconduct myself today.

I think I'll misconduct myself today.
Why don't I break my Hippocratic Oath?
Yield to unbridled passion, lust or both.
Come out in my true colours, make a play,
And up for lost time, for young Mrs South,
Her wares, like Supermarkets', on display
Piquante, provocative, décolletée!
I think I'll misconduct myself today.

Prince, if you will but vouchsafe me the key
Of your Zenana where in beauty vie
Your sloe-eyed wives – forgetting my MD,
I think I'll misconduct myself today.

*T*he late Richard Asher when teaching his students, insisted that before they diagnosed malingering, they should rule out organic disease.

He told them that one day he had to look after his four-year-old daughter Jane (now Jane Asher the actress) whilst his wife was away. He said they would go for a walk and she refused. He chastised her and she still refused. He then dressed her and again she said she wouldn't go for a walk. She claimed she couldn't move her left leg. Before smacking her again, he thought he ought to rule out an organic problem, so he examined her. He discovered he had put both legs in one hole of her knickers.

A Town Council's Housing Committee was discussing amenities on a new municipal estate. Amongst the proposals was one from the Medical Officer of Health for a gentleman's urinal. The world 'gentleman' provoked opposition from a left-wing Labour councillor. This he pursued until the proposal was deferred for consideration at a subsequent meeting of the Committee.

It so happened that the opening of a new public house on the estate took place on the same day as the subsequent meeting. The brewery owners made this something of an occasion. They were exceedingly generous with both food and drink for their invited guests, among whom were the councillor and the Medical Officer of Health. The doctor gave the councillor a lift to the meeting. On the journey the councillor began to feel the effects of hospitality. He remarked to the doctor that the estate was in great need of a public toilet. The doctor reminded him of his opposition to the urinal. To this he responded 'So that's what it was'.

At the evening meeting when the urinal came up for consideration he said, 'I have changed my mind about this and let's have an arsenal as well'.

———— · ✻ · ————

An Irishman's letter to a Family Planning Clinic

Dear Sir,

I wish to apply for an operation to make me sterile. My reasons are numerous, and after seven years of marriage and seven children, I have come to the conclusion that contraceptives are totally useless.

After getting married, I was advised to use the 'Rhythm Method'. Despite trying the tango and the samba, my wife fell pregnant and I ruptured myself doing the cha cha.

A doctor advised using the 'Safe Period'. At the time we were living with in-laws and we had to wait three weeks for a safe period when the house was empty. Needless to say, this did not work.

A lady of several years experience informed us that if we made love while breast feeding we would be all right. It's hardly Newcastle Brown Ale, but I did end up with a clear skin, silky hair and felt very healthy. My wife was pregnant again.

Another old wives' tale we heard was that if my wife jumped up and down after intercourse, it would prevent pregnancy. This she did but ended up with two black eyes and knocked herself out.

So I asked the chemist about the sheath. The chemist demonstrated how easy it was to use, so I brought a packet home. My wife fell pregnant again, which didn't surprise me. I fail to see how a sheath spread over the thumb, as the chemist showed me, can prevent babies.

She was then supplied with the coil, and after several unsuccessful attempts to fit it, we discovered that the coil had a left-hand thread and the wife a right.

The Dutch Cap came next. We were very hopeful of this as it did not interfere with our sex life at all. But it did give the wife many headaches. Despite having the largest size available, it was still too tight across her forehead.

You will appreciate her problem and mine. At present we have reverted to oral sex, but as you will agree, just talking about it is no substitute for the real thing.

*A*n SHO at the Royal Free, Dr. D. P. Mikhailidis, recently doing nominal research in the *Index Medicus*, came across some oft-quoted authors with strange-sounding names.

*'I'd appreciate it if you didn't tell my wife
about this.'*

During 1978, for instance, D. Phil published thirteen papers while his brother M. Phil managed only two. M.R. Path published five, but his cousin F.R. Path, who in 1977 published two, stayed mute.

The Chir brothers did well. M. Chir published twice and the younger and more ambitious B. Chir published four papers, a slight comedown after his seven in 1977 and six in 1976.

Twins, B. Pharm and M. Pharm, managed a paper each last year and B.V. Med made his annual contribution to veterinary medicine.

Dr Mikhailidis's finest discovery was the three authors, F.I. Biol, B.M. Sci and F.R. Psych. What a pity that poor Psych, like the Path cousins, loses his last initial, a C, because of the *Index's* policy of not using more than two initials per surname.

A Residential Home for elderly people had a social evening with games, music, dancing and a bar.

A ninety-three year old came up to the bar and asked for a whisky with water, four parts whisky and one part water.

'No', said the nurse in charge, 'you surely mean four parts water and one part whisky'.

'Oh no', said the old lady, 'four parts whisky and one part water. I can hold my whisky but I can't hold my water'.

A middle-aged Irish woman approached her GP complaining of soreness in her 'back passage'.

The GP, taking the case history with some care, enquired if the discomfort was in the rectal or the genital passage. This evoked the reply, 'Sure doctor, you're quite right, it's in the Gentleman's passage'.

W hile assisting with an emergency caesarian section in the labour ward, the scrub nurse noticed that when the table was tipped sideways, one of the legs of the patient was falling off the edge. When she asked someone to lift up the leg, she felt a hand trying to wrench her own foot from the ground and very nearly had to conduct the instrumentation from below the table.

A n eminent New York surgeon had recommended removal of the gall-bladder to a wealthy patient who asked how much it would cost. The surgeon replied, 'My fee for this operation is 5,000 dollars'. As there was no untoward reaction on the part of the patient to this, the surgeon immediately added, 'Of course, if we find gall-stones then the fee will be 10,000 dollars'.

'There's nothing I can do for you – you <u>are</u> a duck.'

*'Don't be horrible — you'd want to show off
if you had something new. Go on, ask him
about his new heart.'*

W hen I was a medical student we lived near Cork in Eire.

My father arranged for me to join a Dr Murphy on his ward round in the Home for Protestant Incurables in that city.

Arriving early I noticed an old Irish lady whose cottage was near our house. 'Well Hannah,' I said, 'how are you getting on in here and what do you think of Dr Murphy?'

'Dr Murphy is it? Oh a grand man, a lovely man entirely. And I'll tell you he's a very clever – yes indeed a fine doctor. I can assure you that when Dr Murphy says they're going to die, they're dead within the week.'

W ith all doctors sometime in their professional life, doubts are cast upon their diagnostic ability. The following was one of the oddest examples. I had been called to see the wife of a middle-aged gentleman who had recently moved into a council flat in our area. After I examined her and prescribed for a relatively minor complaint, the husband said to me, 'Doctor, I want you to come and look at this carpet, and I want you to give me a line for the Social Security saying that this carpet is a danger!'. I looked at the offending carpet which was too small for the living room; there was a gap between the edge of the carpet and the wall. He then went on to say that his wife often liked to look out of the window, and when she got up she frequently tripped over the edge of the carpet. Shaking my head, I said, 'Well, that carpet should really be your responsibility. All you have to do is to get a packet of carpet tacks and nail it down so your wife doesn't trip over it'. This seemed to upset the gentleman considerably and he said, 'That's not good enough, doctor, I want a second opinion'. To this I replied, 'I suppose then you will be asking for a carpet fitter to be sent'.

*C*oroner's Officer to pathologist: 'Does death from motor neurone disease mean that the lady died as the result of a road traffic accident?'.

A doctor in a busy casualty unit on a particularly busy day was examining a male opera singer who was complaining of back pain. The doctor wanted to see the offending area so began lifting up the man's shirt and then the man's vest. Only when the 'vest' was up to the man's neck with no sign of bare flesh, to the distress of the patient, did he discover it was his underpants. 'I think I moved him up a couple of octaves!' the doctor later commented, his head held low with shame.

'I'm only a shadow of the man I was before
my operation Doctor.'

'I wish you'd called me sooner, Mrs.
Moodie.'

Dr Ben Adam

(With apologies to Leigh Hunt)

Dr Ben Adam, may his List increase,
In Life's high summer, kind, beloved of all,
Dreaming one night in unaccustomed peace
Woke with a start to yet another call.
This time, alas, 'twas not Miss Archer's pain,
As often times before disturbed the Sleeper
Nor Jack Hogg, drunk, thumping his wife again.
Tonight a different caller!
    'Twas the Reaper!

Saint Peter met him warmly at the Gate.
'Good Doctor, kindly tell me in what fashion
You lived. And were your good deeds small or great,
To help me in preparing your Citation?'
Ben Adam smiled and slowly made reply
'I worked,' he said, 'sans glamour and sans fuss.
I'm here because demand outstripped supply,
Write me as one who loved the NHS.'

The Saint half smiled, the morrow dawned, and when
He wakened up to joy and ecstasy,
And read Celestial Orders, Dr Ben
Beheld, writ on the Detail for the Day,
Of kindred souls immortalized, a List,
Those newly come to Paradise that must
Consult the Heavenly Psychiatrist,
And Lo! Ben Adam's name led all the rest!

*E*xaminers in Part II of the MRCP (UK) (Membership of the Royal College of Physicians) are expected to cover various subjects during the oral examination. One of these is an understanding of physiological principles. Wishing to introduce a discussion on physiological effects of exercise, the examiner asked a candidate what he thought was the most common cause for breathlessness in a healthy person. The candidate was clearly flummoxed by the question and suggested a number of rare medical conditions. The examiner, hoping to simplify the matter, explained to the candidate that he himself had been breathless the previous day (omitting to mention that his breathlessness had been induced by jogging). The candidate's face lit up as it became quite clear he now knew the appropriate answer. 'Ah, yes Sir, of course' he said, 'Cardiac neurosis'.

*M*y own particular interest is microsurgery for infertility. Whilst this is rewarding work it can occasionally result in the most acute embarrassment.

One Saturday morning, I went into my building society. The girl behind the counter asked me to have a seat since the business was rather involved and I would have to see the manager. Whilst I was waiting, a long queue developed. At the end of the queue was an extremely attractive young woman with a push chair. She beamed broadly and waved. I waved back in a rather non-committal manner. For the life of me

'Do I ever feel depressed? What kind of a
question is that? I'm a lemming.'

'Is that your neuro-surgeon, dear?'

I could not think who she was. Realizing this, and in an effort to help, she called across in a loud voice, 'This is one of yours you know,' pointing to the baby.

The whole queue turned towards me and to make matters even worse, she then added, 'But absolute magic, I am pregnant again. My husband and I are moving south'.

I left the building society and to this day I do not know who she was.

A week later, I returned to conclude my business. This time I took with me a newspaper and, joining the queue, hid behind it until I got to the front of the queue which seemed to take ages. When I got there, the girl said, 'Yes sir, can I help?'. I then realized I was in the wrong building society and that the one I should have been in was next door. 'Yes,' I said, 'I would like to open an account' and deposited £5, which is still there!

*T*he Golders Green Hippodrome is hot and dark. A girl faints. A mother screams, 'Help! Help! Is there a doctor in the house?' A young man rushes forward and the mother looks up to him, imploring, 'You want to meet a nice girl?'.

A newly appointed Family Planning Clinic nurse was working with a lady doctor at a busy clinic in the centre of Birmingham, an area not renowned for clear or concise speech.

Leaning over the patient, performing a speculum examination, the doctor, perhaps mumbling a little, requested a 'copper T' (a now superseded intra-uterine contraception device).

The nurse disappeared from the room and to the great irritation of the doctor, who remained with the speculum in situ (i.e. in the patient), was gone an unconscionably long time. Eventually, however, the door opened and the doctor turned to see the nurse reappearing bearing a cup o' tea!

· ✀ ·

Failed Sterilization

I had just booked a patient into the ante-natal clinic in her fifth pregnancy.

'Have you thought about sterilization?' I asked.

'My husband has had a vasectomy,' she replied.

'Oh,' I said, 'and who did that?'

'You did,' she said.

'Good heavens,' I said, 'this is serious. You must get him up to see me.'

'There's not much point,' she said, 'I don't live with him now.'

'Have I told you about my operation?'

Not long ago our surgical registrar was asked to see a geriatric patient in a hospital in our group. By the time he got round to seeing her it was evening. He was dressed casually in a polo neck sweater, trousers and a black bomber jacket.

He had been called as the patient had had a rectal bleed and a surgical cause was to be excluded. Having done a rectal examination, he held up his gloved hand and rather solemnly announced, 'I am pleased to say, madam, you do not have a surgical problem'.

'Thank you very much indeed', replied the somewhat disorientated lady, and turning to the nurse said, 'Nurse, by the way, who was that, the vicar?'.

The other day – well yesterday actually – one of my regular attenders hobbled in clutching his groin, and announced that he had 'got trouble with his moles doctor'.

Now I was slightly curious to know why he was clutching his groin with a mole or moles, and my curiosity was further whetted when he announced that they were on 'his hummocks'. Well, I have heard them called lots of things before, I thought, but never that!

I suspected that whatever they were, they were probably not serious or I would no doubt have seen them on one of his frequent previous attendances. However, perhaps he had been alerted by publicity about the dangers of melanoma, and perhaps I would fetch out Dr Rona Mackay's excellent illustrated little book on benign naevi to prove the point.

However, he continued, the moles in question were actually the black furry kind that dig holes in gardens. In his garden, he was the proud possessor of two hummocks of the small hill variety. His hummocks were known the length and breadth of the street as a haven for wild life.

Unfortunately, his love of nature did not extend to small black furry mammals, and as they were digging up his hummocks, he had deteremined to be rid of them.

Now I was beginning to warm to this consultation, having had the same problem, at least with the moles, in my own garden. Had he tried sticking holly leaves in the runs? No he had not. What about mothballs in the burrows — guaranteed to deter moles and underground flying insects? No. What about planting *euphorbia lathyrus*, a horrible looking and smelling plant that makes them leave in disgust that you should plant something so unaesthetic? What about a child's windmill in the ground? Apparently they do not like the vibration and move next door. None of these had worked for me but perhaps he could try! In the end our cat saw our moles off, but he had not got one of these either.

In fact he had tried none of these remedies, but had resorted to the age-old trick of trying to kill them. His particular method relied on the well-known fact that moles always dig their burrows at three o'clock in the afternoon. The plan was to wait for the three o'clock shift to start up, look out for the shifting earth, and then run out to the hummocks and stab them with a garden fork.

*'Do tell us about your operation, Wendy —
we're all still on waiting lists.'*

Unfortunately his moles were either working to British Summer Time or had not heard of this well-known piece of country lore. It could be that they were stuffed full of worms already from the nature reserve, and had decided to lie low for a bit.

In any event, he had several false alarms, and had rushed out on so many occasions that not only had he fully aerated his lawn, but had given himself an inguinal hernia in the process.

Hence the reason for clutching his groin.

I do not suppose the surgeon I have referred him to will believe me either.

*H*ave you ever done something so awful in the surgery that you cringe inwardly at the memory of it?

Well I have, plenty of times, but I am only going to own up to one incident now, when the passage of time has helped to reduce the immediate awfulness and convert it into an amusing and not quite so embarrassing episode.

This particular faux pas occured fairly early in my G.P. career, on my second day as a brand new, wet-behind-the-consulting-desk, G.P. trainee, to be exact.

I was supposed to be sitting in on my trainer, and halfway through the surgery was enjoying the luxury of watching someone else at work, while not having to do too much myself, except wonder at the apparently trivial nature of the complaints. Unfortunately

I was awakened from my false sense of security by the receptionist telephoning through with an urgent call. I imagine my trainer was already a little delayed by my presence, and the prospect of returning to a restless waiting room later on prompted him to ask me if I would like to carry on with his surgery while he was out?

Well, yes, please I would! Having sat in on a whole three surgeries (nearly) by now, I was actually quite keen to give it a try. Off he went and I pressed the buzzer for the next patient.

I was casually wondering why her notes were twice as heavy as any other in the box, when in she walked. It was immediately apparent that she was not expecting to see me, and this impression was closely followed by the feeling that she did not particularly want to see me either!

I do not recall this good lady's name, but I expect it was double-barrelled, or if it wasn't it should have been or she would have liked it to have been. At any rate she looked fairly imposing as she was heavily built and wore a fur coat and the sort of glasses that go up inquisitorially at the corners. Probably her build and temperament accounted at least in part for her hypertension which was what she had come about.

She paused in the doorway. 'So, you're not Doctor Jones!' she observed. I agreed, this was not my name. (In fact it was not his either, but this is my story!) I invited her in, reassuring her that indeed I was a doctor, albeit not the one she had expected or wanted to see. Furthermore, if the emergency was short enough and close enough, and she stayed long enough, she might even get to see her personal physician. In

*'He'd been very depressed lately about his
high cholesterol level.'*

'Well, the doctors were right — they said I'd
be out of hospital inside a fortnight.'

any case I promised faithfully to convey her requests and my findings to the said man immediately upon his return. Thus only partially reassured, she stepped suspiciously in.

After depositing her not inconsiderable bulk on the chair beside the desk (see, you can tell it was a training practice with the chair next to, not opposite, the doctor!), she told me that Doctor Jones (still not his real name) usually took her blood pressure. Well I was quite pleased that this was all she wanted, as I felt sure this was within my capabilities. Having reassured us both on this score, I invited her to roll up her sleeve. This was my first mistake, you cannot fit a sphygmomanometer cuff over a fur coat. Would Madam care to slip her arm out of the coat as this cuff seems rather small? Madam obliged with scarcely concealed scorn. Mistake number two, you cannot fit a sphygmomanometer cuff over the arm distal to the desk, otherwise the rubber tubing will not stretch and the instrument falls on the lap. Would Madam care to slip the other arm out of the coat as the tubing seems rather short? Madam obliged with unconcealed scorn.

Now I had been looking forward to one part of this, and that was the part when the nifty electronic sphygmo started to bleep between systolic and diastolic, as I had seen demonstrated by the still absent trainer. It was a new toy, and I felt fairly sure that it would impress, at least it would explain why I was not using a stethoscope. Unfortunately I had failed to notice one rather vital point with this marvel of electronic wizardry, and that was that it was necessary to position an arrow on the cuff over the brachial artery!

After several bleepless attempts to find the blood

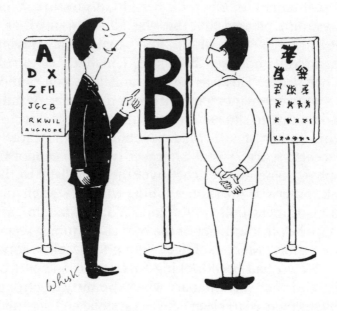

'This one is for testing football referees.'

pressure, madam's arm was beginning to look slightly cyanosed, and she was starting to grimace with a mixture of pain and contempt, or so it seemed to me. Having been subjected to the same treatment by way of a physiology practical as a student, I appreciated that the pain was geniune enough.

I decided to cut my losses and take the no doubt by now raised pressure with a conventional mercury column model. Unfortunately it was well hidden and no doubt my rummaging around under the couch did not contribute favourably to the situation. Still no matter, blood pressure eventually taken, decision made to leave treatment exactly as is, and both patient and doctor glad to be nearly finished with latter's first consultation in G.P.

Now here is the worst part, you might have thought that the tyro G.P. would have wanted to leave well alone at this stage, but no, ever a glutton for punishment, he pressed on. In an attempt to salvage some credibility from the situation he (that is I) brightly suggested it might be a good idea to make one or two other checks as part of the hypertensive well-person's check up. The opthalmoscope on the desk beckoned.

Madam uneasily agreed to allow her fundi to be examined. Mistake number three, never investigate unnecessarily. I thought that she was wiggling around rather more than was strictly necessary as I took good care to visualise the complete optic disc. I even swopped hands to examine the other eye.

When I had finished, and sat back to record the fairly unremarkable findings, I realised with a sinking feeling why she had been so mobile. Face saving had turned to face painting, and I had drawn a series of neat concentric circles under her eyes with the pen I had been holding in my hand at the same time! I had even swopped the pen around at the same time as the opthalmoscope!

To tell or not to tell, this was the question. I still wonder even now if I did the right thing. Perhaps it would have been better after all to allow her to have gone and wonder how or why she had acquired quink on the cheeks in the privacy of her own home. She might even have believed that it was part of the examination! As it was, valour proved the better part of discretion, and I owned up to the mistake. Some would call it honesty, others would call it foolishness; in any case, she was not impressed!

My first patient backed carefully out of the door, dabbing at her cheeks with a moistened handkerchief. As she left and I rang for the next patient, I reflected that there was more to this job than met the eye!

*I*n 1947 the x-ray department was a very different place compared with what it is today. Screen examinations were carried out in darkness. Patients awaiting their turn for barium meal examination were lined up on a bench against the wall inside the screening room. High voltage current to the x-ray apparatus was carried by open conductors suspended from the ceiling. In appropriate atmospheric conditions

'Sixty thousand pounds' worth of scientific research and you thought we were going to let you take the baby home?'

sparking occurred across these conductors with quite a large 'crack'. This happened often enough to be hardly noticed by the staff.

I was screening the first barium meal patient of the session in one of the London hospitals when a spark occurred between the conductors with the usual 'crack'. The little old lady who was next in line for examination jumped off her seat and hurriedly left the room. Indeed we found that she had dressed quickly and left the hospital. Next morning an eminent neurologist with his retinue of registrars came to the department to find out how we conducted our x-ray examinations. His Irish charwoman had attended for a barium meal the previous day and had returned home in a state of terror. He was astonished when she told him that patients were being taken into a darkened room and were being shot.

*P*lanning a new hospital causes a great deal of anxiety for medical staff as planners seem to have little idea of how we work. We were poring over the plan of the x-ray department and could not understand the function of a room furnished with chairs and small tables. This was sent back to the architect for enlightenment. He explained that this was the 'Barium Meal Room'.

*T*he lady was referred to my Outpatient Clinic requesting sterilization. I needed to know what sort of contraceptive precautions the lady was taking at the time. 'Oh, I leave all that to my husband' she said. 'He uses Duraglit.'

*A*n ample coloured lady came along to the Gynaecology Clinic and turned out to have an erosion of the cervix. The size of her physique was matched by the intensity of her modesty. I was unable to get her to remove any clothing whatsoever, she would only provide very limited access to her genitalia, so that the introduction of the vaginal speculum was not easy for either of us. Nonetheless I was able to cauterize the cervix satisfactorily and, as always, this was entirely painless and produced a small whiff of smoke from the speculum. At this stage the patient, still fully clothed, looked down at what I was doing and said, 'Hey Doc, you push that thing in much further and you'll knock my hat off! Anyway, what are you doing down there − electing a Pope?'.

'Well, it looks as if Mr. Jenkinson has rejected his new heart.'

*'One doesn't feel so guilty when one finds
another smoker to talk to.'*

I was carrying out a barium examination when the old man on the table pleaded 'Please doctor don't operate on me just now'. I reassured him that I had no intention of doing so in the dark and whilst wearing such clumsy gloves.

A n indication of the early maturity of children in the 1980's is provided by the following conversation between two five-year-olds.

First child: 'I found a contraceptive yesterday on the veranda'.

Second child: 'What's a veranda?'

I entered the theatre to find the theatre sisters contemplating the immense form of a lady overflowing the operating table on both sides. 'It is my constant prayer that I shall never become like that,' said the senior sister in awe. I could not refrain from commenting, 'This kind can only come by prayer *and fasting*!'.

*I*n the 1950's a Thomas's doctor, doing his first job in Hereford, was required to give an anaesthetic to a young man with a dislocated bone in his wrist. As the consultant orthopaedic surgeon stepped forward, satisfied his patient was unconscious, the patient leaped off the table and, brushing everyone aside, ran down the corridor and into the street. The young doctor caught up with him just short of the Cathedral Close. The patient, clad only in an open-backed theatre gown, cried, 'I'm dreadfully sorry, I've never had an anaesthetic before'. To which the doctor replied, 'Don't worry old chap, I've never given one before'.

*I*n a surgical out-patients clinic an old gentleman pleaded with me, 'I 'ope you ain't goin ter take anyfink art, Sir, I've 'ad firty-free fings art orlready'.

'Thirty-three?' I echoed incredulously.

'Yus, Sir — firty-two teef an' a kidney.'

A chunk of plaster from the ceiling of one of the cubicles in our old paediatric ward fell onto the bed which was occupied by a little girl of five; fortunately she was not in bed at the time. Shortly afterwards, she was overheard on the telephone saying, 'And you know Nan, if I had been in bed they would have had to take me to hospital'.

'Can I get him to ring you back? He's trying
to out-stare the dog again.'

'If I had known he was going to charge for every prescription he wouldn't have got the damn thing.'

A young house officer was sitting in out-patients. He yawned and pressed his buzzer to call in the next patient. A rather small, plump man entered and sat down.

'Now, what can I do for you?' asked the doctor.

'My GP says I have something called Peyronie's Disease,' said the rather embarrassed man.

At that point the house officer felt the presence of his consultant at his shoulder.

'What have we here?' the specialist asked.

'Peyronie's Disease,' the house officer replied and showed the notes and the GP's letter to his superior.

The consultant burst into a fit of uncontrollable laughter and staggered from the room.

Bewildered, the young house officer looked down at the notes and the letter. He followed the example of his superior and burst out laughing.

The patient stood, 'humphed', turned and strode out of the room.

The doctor looked down at the letter again. 'It cannot be,' he thought.

But it was. The patient's name was Mr Bentcock.

*'You have lovely teeth. You should take
anti-depressants more often.'*

A Rep Reflects

I dread to visit Dr Heal
He constantly cuts short my spiel.

I like to visit Dr Fender
He's rough, his Secretary tender.

I hate to visit Dr Campbell's
He spills his coffee on my samples.

I like to call on Doc. Scott, she
Can have carte blanche to sample me.

I hate to call on Dr Arnott
He is discourtesy incarnate.

What a cute number Dr Spence is!
I entertain her on expenses.

I'm no good friend of Doc Weingartner's
That goes as well for all his partners.

How nice to call at Dr Jackson's
He *reads* my BMJ abstractions.

I'm a bit scared of Dr Keith
They said he choked a Rep to death.

I love to call on Dr Dix
36   24   36.

I hate to call on Dr Fenwick
He thinks most illness istrogenic.

I like to call at Dr Evans's
With gin and tonic for elevenses.

Dr de Vere I find Draconian
I'm Comprehensive, he's Etonian.

And so the cat jumps! Lastly I'll come
To kind old Dr Burroughs, welcome.

One of the problems sometimes encountered in the laboratory is the situation where a patient suffering from one illness, maybe a long term one like rheumatoid arthritis or high blood pressure, develops some unrelated acute problem and is investigated for that. Sometimes the person ordering the test puts the original diagnosis and not the recent problem on the request form. On one such occasion a request was received for a urine bacteriology test on a patient where the only information given was the one word 'Schizophrenia'. After a few minutes thought the Microbiologist proceeded to return the form to its originator with the comment 'We are in two minds as to what to do with this specimen'.

Mr Brown was a young man who suffered from schizophrenia. In addition to hearing voices and having unusual beliefs, he also suffered from a condition (sometimes known as Capgras syndrome) in which he believed that people he knew well had been replaced by exact doubles that looked the same but were different people. On his first admission to hospital he improved with treatment and realized that his beliefs were false. His psychiatrist discharged him to follow-up out-patient care and encouraged him to return to work as a petrol pump attendant.

Two weeks later, Mr Brown's psychiatrist was visited by his brother, an identical twin, who was also a psychiatrist but lived in a different city. On his way home he pulled into a petrol station to fill up before his long return journey. After filling the tank the attendant turned to him and jokingly asked where he was travelling to so late at night and also discussed his own feelings and how he was coping with life. The twin brother realized that he had been misidentified, explained that he was not the doctor that Mr Brown thought he was, but happened to be his identical twin brother and practised in a different city. There was an uneasy pause and no more words were exchanged.

Two days later Mr Brown presented as an emergency to the local casualty department saying that people were again playing tricks on him and even his psychiatrist had now been replaced by a double. A relapse of his schizophrenia was diagnosed immediately and he was admitted to hospital compulsorily. Three days later, when he saw his real psychiatrist again, it was realized that his beliefs probably had some basis and he was accordingly reassured. But he would have none of it. 'You're all impostors,' he said, 'now one of you has admitted it the rest of you can own up'.

A very young and very anxious girl was being counselled by a rather senior WRNS officer who was overhead saying, 'But my dear, you must remember Lady Hamilton was not a member of the WRNS'.

'Can't grumble really — I tried to jump the
varicose veins queue.'

*T*he late surgeon Captain Desmond Curran, RNVR (Consultant Psychiatrist to the Navy) in a paper on 'operational strain' recounted a new criterion of improvement, or at least one not explicitly set forth in the medical literature. The scene was North Russia after a famous convoy with many casualties. His medical informant told him that some concern was felt about the survivors who were much shaken and, it was felt, unhealthily addicted to the discussion of their terrible experiences, coupled with criticisms of those who might be held responsible. One day the chief petty officer announced, 'The men are all right again, Sir, they have gone back to talking ...' and he used a less polite word than sex.

*T*he eminent psychiatrist, the late Sir David Henderson, was demonstrating a case of manic depression to a class of final-year students in 1935. The patient was in an acute manic phase and when asked if he would care to talk to the students, without hesitation he began, 'Ladies and gentlemen, there are three types of insanity. I am an example of the first type, the nurses in this institution belong to the second type and Professor Henderson is the worst of the whole lot'.

The scene – a railway carriage.

The man with the wild eyes and his tie knot up under his left ear, sat between the quiet, purposeful-visaged companions with peaked caps, and gibbered quietly to himself. I peered surreptitiously at the neat lettering on those peaked caps, recognized the mental home and regarded the victim the furtive sympathy.

'Name of Potts,' he said, nodding and laughing in a high-pitched voice. 'I am my own grandfather.'

I started slightly. 'There, there, then,' said one of the asylum attendants soothingly, 'look at the nice cows in that field'.

The train rattled on and the wild-eyed man shook off the patting hand and leaned forward earnestly. He seemed desirous that I should attend. I listened patiently. 'I have just discovered it,' he added impressively. 'I met a widow with a grown daughter. Now, I married that widow. It was this that started all the trouble, because my father also married – the grown daughter.'

I nodded kindly and offered him a cigarette. 'It is permitted?' I asked the attendants. It was permitted. The wild-eyed man carried on after I had held a match to the weed. 'You understand that I married the widow, my father married the widow's daughter. That made my wife the mother-in-law of her father-in-law. My step-daughter became my step-mother. My father became my step-son.'

I stopped smoking and stared fixedly with sagging jaw. He laughed ghoulishly and went on.

'Then my wife's daughter, my step-mother through marrying my father, had a son. That boy, naturally, became my step-brother because he was my father's son. Got that?' Hoarsely, I ventured that I followed so far.

'But,' pursued the wild-eyed man looking wilder, 'that boy, being the son of my wife's daughter was therefore her grandson. That,' he burst out passionately, 'made me grandfather to my own step-brother. Now listen,' he entreated, laying an eager forefinger in his palm and tapping. 'My wife then had a son. Besides being my son, he was brother to my wife's daughter – the one who married my father – yet she was my mother. Therefore I was my own son's nephew. Besides being the brother of my mother, he was also her grandson.' He lay back in his seat and goggled with a petrified gaze. 'As my wife's daughter's grandson, he was therefore his own mother's great grandson.' I wiped my brow with my handkerchief. 'Great Scott,' I muttered aghast.

'I should think so. Then what? In addition to being my wife's husband I was her grandson. *She* was the mother of her daughter, who was my mother by marrying my father. Who am I? That's what I want to know. Another thing. As my father married the step-sister of my son he is brother-in-law to his grandson.' He began laughing wildly and commenced tearing the cigarette to shreds.

'Look here,' I gasped weakly. 'You mustn't.' 'My own son,' he bawled, 'he is the son of my grandmother. Mad! The whole world is stark, raving mad. And my father married my step-daughter. Therefore my father is my son. In short, I am my father's father. Therefore I must be my own grandfather'.

A naval petty officer reported to the sick bay complaining of a nasty rash round both groins. The doctor asked him what he used to wash his underwear. 'Bilge cleaner, Sir.'

'You must stop using that at once and get some proper washing powder.'

'Does that mean I must get a new shampoo as well?'

M alingering was a serious offence in the Royal Navy, particularly during the war when it was still 'punishable by death or such other punishment as their Lordships may hereinafter determine'. The distinction between physical and mental illness and frank malingering was not always clear and many cases must have been given the benefit of the doubt since one had to be certain of the diagnosis.

I had one such case. A man who pretended he had diabetes and had fooled the staff of an EMS hospital to such an extent that he was given insulin. He confessed when we found him out and within twenty-four hours an armed escort appeared and marched him out of the ward in handcuffs. The therapeutic effect on the other patients was little short of miraculous.

To this day I am uncertain about another man who was on his way back to his ship when he telephoned the hospital to ask if he could return as he had just discovered that he was wearing two left boots

'You're a mess, Mr. Bulstrode. It would be cheaper to knock you down and start again.'

and if he reported in this state he would be charged with being improperly dressed. He was told to continue his journey and a signal was sent to his captain to expect a sailor with two left feet.

When malingering was suspected but not proved, various pseudonyms were sometimes used in the case notes such as 'oscillating plumbism' or 'haemato-dementia'. In one such case, the medical officer in charge of the hospital was a retired surgeon rear-admiral who had been out of touch with clinical medicine for many years and when he read a discharge letter which said that oscillating plumbism was suspected in this case, he sent for the author of the letter and asked, 'Can there be any question of lead poisoning in this case?'.

In another instance, a WRNS officer was being a great trial to the doctors. The medical officer in charge of her case wrote in the notes, 'This woman is a bloody nuisance,' and left the folder lying on the ward desk. The temptation to have a look was too much. She took her own discharge from hospital the following day.

*I*n the nineteen thirties, an Edinburgh student was taking his final examination in clinical medicine. The examiners were two very senior physicians, both in their early sixties. The elder of the two, Dr W. was a benign, well nourished gentleman who believed that good food and improved nutrition would cure all the ills of mankind. He was really a bit of a humbug, but was always very courteous and had the perfect bedside manner. In short, he was the ideal consultant for Dr Snoddy and the rich widows of Tannochbrae.

The other, Dr M., was a thin, ascetic-looking and irascible little man who was feared by everyone but was a superb teacher and clinician, the obvious choice of Dr Finlay when the diagnosis was obscure.

The student thought that he was getting on quite well with his case until be referred to the patient as an old man. Dr W. then asked, 'When do you think old age begins?'. 'Fifty,' was the prompt reply. 'Don't you think that seems a little young?' 'Well, perhaps sixty, Sir.' Dr M. could contain himself no longer. 'Boy. Are you under the impression that you are being examined by a pair of blithering old idiots?'

*P*ractitioners in the Scottish Highlands and Islands have to be self sufficient and very astute and resourceful in more ways than one. A very colourful character on the Isle of Skye had a private patient who seldom paid his bills. When a particularly large sum was owing the doctor decided that he would have some of it in kind and went off to fish in his patient's stretch of river. He was casting in the best salmon pool when the owner appeared and said, 'Are you enjoying the fishing?'

'Yes, yes, but not many are biting,' as he carried on fishing.

'Do you know that the fishing here belong to me?'

'Does it now, does it now, that's very interesting.'

'It costs me a lot of money.'

'Does it now, does it now? If you pay as much for it as you do for your medical attention, you're getting it damned cheap.'

Some years ago a keen young nurse, acting as a runner on her first day in theatre, was instructed by a consultant anaesthetist during a tricky operation on a baby to go to the blood bank fridge, get a pint of blood, warm it up and bring it to theatre. After several minutes, whilst the baby's need for blood had intensified, the nurse had still not returned. Upon investigation the diligent pupil nurse was discovered simmering the whole pint of blood in a saucepan in the theatre suite kitchen.

'Your blood pressure is up by quite a bit,
Mr. Fraser.'

On a snowy December day a well known surgeon in a northern city discarded his bowler and shoes in favour of a flat cap and clogs (this was in the nineteen thirties). He was doing his Christmas shopping when an elderly woman was knocked down by a bicycle as she crossed the street. As he bent down to see if he could be of any assistance he was pushed aside by a small boy who said, 'Out of the way monkey-face, I'm a Boy Scout.' After telling this story with some relish he said, 'Do you know, when I got home I looked in the mirror, and my face is a bit like a monkey's.'

*'I don't think his injuries are too serious —
he has just lapped Lauda and Watson and is
about to pass Rosberg.'*